SCALE SHA

GRADE 1

for piano

Based on the requirements for Grade 1 of
the Associated Board of the Royal Schools of Music

This book © Copyright 2001 Chester Music
Order No. CH62964
ISBN 0-7119-9022-0

Cover and template design by Phil Gambrill.
Music engraved by Note-orious Productions Ltd.
Printed in the United Kingdom.

CHESTER MUSIC
(A division of Music Sales Limited)
8/9 Frith Street, London W1D 3JB

by
FREDERICK
STOCKEN

This series of books shows scale shapes using the Stocken Method and is based on the technical exercises required by the piano grades of the Associated Board of the Royal Schools of Music. Even without the goal of an examiniation, the scales chosen by the Associated Board provide carefully thought-out exercises at eight levels which provide an excellent basis for daily study. It is hoped that the principles established here will soon be extended to other compilations of scales including jazz scales.

I always loved playing scales and other technical exercises as a child – and still do. However, when I came to teach the piano and organ I quickly discovered that many students, especially children, find them to be drudgery. Although the repetitive nature of the exercises is often cited as the main cause of boredom, I believe that this is not often in reality the root of the problem. The student who complains of the tedium of repetition when practising scales might well be the same person who has a fitness programme that involves plenty of repetition and which is found to be most enjoyable.

The mental block many students have with practising scales is not the repetitiveness as such, but the actual technical difficulties involved in reading musical notation and translating this into the physical shapes of the scales themselves. It is these difficulties that seem to prevent the satisfying rhythm of repetition and growing control that the student might find so rewarding when lifting weights or practising kicking a ball into a net.

The method I have invented provides a system which allows the student to concentrate exclusively on the physical shapes of the technical exercise and, in consequence, to focus on the acquisition of 'good legato, even fingers, firm tone and a musical curve' – the criteria specified by the Associated Board as 'the essential features for playing scales and arpeggios well'. In short, I have found that this method helps to make scales become fun.

The Stocken Method is not designed to be a substitute for the acquisition of the ability to read staff notation. *In fact the opposite is the case.* I have found that using this method, which so explicitly presents the physical shapes of different keys at the keyboard, actually helps fix these shapes in the student's mind so that playing from musical notation in the context of a piece or sight-reading actually becomes easier.

However idealistic a teacher may be that a student will learn a scale or technical exercise from staff notation, experience shows that the simplest method of introducing a new scale or other technical exercise is often for the teacher physically to play the exercise demonstrating the new shape for the student to copy. The Stocken Method not only removes this stage of teaching, saving valuable time during lessons, but also gives the student a system for the exercise that he or she will be confident of being able to re-read when the teacher has gone.

At the earlier stages of learning, a simple scale may involve ledger lines or other symbols that are far in advance of the pieces a student may be playing. This is the case right from the beginning when the introduction of a C major scale of two octaves for instance will use a great many more notes in different octaves than the student will have encountered in staff notation. Many students at much higher levels continue to find key signatures and other aspects of staff notation confusing and find the simplicity of this method to be of great help.

In fact one of the revolutionary aspects of the Stocken Method is that the complications of staff notation are no longer linked to the often quite different physical complications of actually playing a given scale. This means that scales which have, until now, seemed more difficult than others, mainly because of the complexity of their representation using staff notation, are now, using this method, suddenly found to be easier. The implication of this for the order in which scales have traditionally been introduced to the student is far-reaching.

Frederick Stocken.

The Associated Board of the Royal Schools of Music list the following requirements for Grade 1 in its piano syllabus:

SCALES, ARPEGGIOS AND BROKEN CHORDS:
from memory.

SCALES:
Major and minor (melodic *or* harmonic at candidate's choice):
(i) with each hand separately, up and down (L.H. may, at the candidate's choice, be played down and up) in the following keys:

> C, G, D, F majors (two octaves)
> A, D minors (two octaves)

(ii) in contrary motion with both hands beginning and ending on the key-note (unison), in the key of C major only (one octave).

ARPEGGIOS:
The common chords of C, G and F majors, and A and D minors, in root position only, with each hand separately (one octave).

BROKEN CHORDS:
Formed from the chords of C, G and F majors, and A and D minors, with each hand separately, according to the following pattern:

Contents

C MAJOR SCALE

Hands separately: 2 Octaves. The left hand may start at the top or bottom of the scale at the candidate's choice.

♩ = 60 *(minimum speed recommended by the ABRSM)*

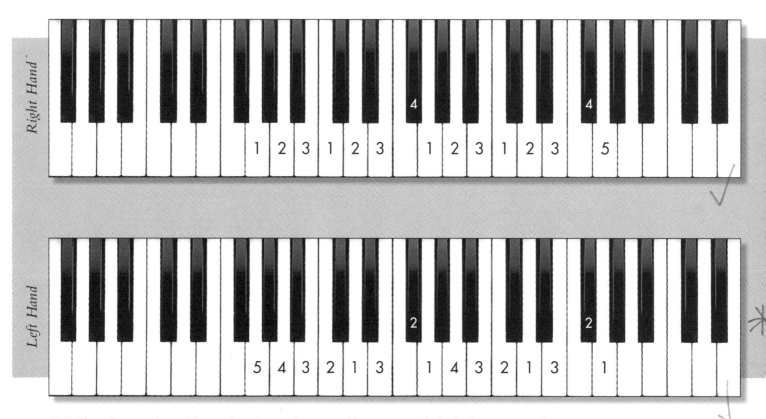

G MAJOR SCALE

Hands separately: 2 Octaves. The left hand may start at the top or bottom of the scale at the candidate's choice.

N.B. The scales are written without a time signature in groups of four quavers with the final note as a crotchet.

D MAJOR SCALE

Hands separately: 2 Octaves. The left hand may start at the top or bottom of the scale at the candidate's choice.

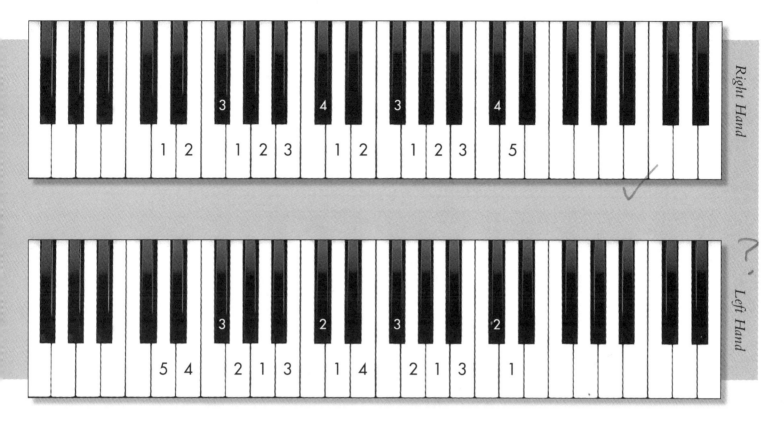

F MAJOR SCALE

Hands separately: 2 Octaves. The left hand may start at the top or bottom of the scale at the candidate's choice.

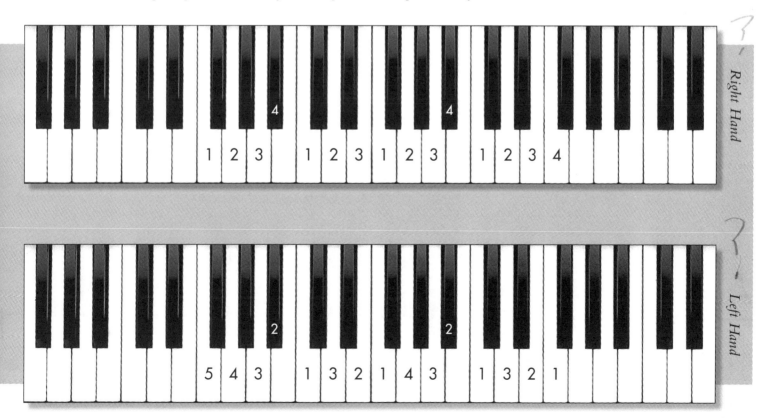

The candidate may choose to play either the harmonic minor OR the melodic minor scale.

A MINOR HARMONIC SCALE

Hands separately: 2 Octaves. The left hand may start at the top or bottom of the scale at the candidate's choice.

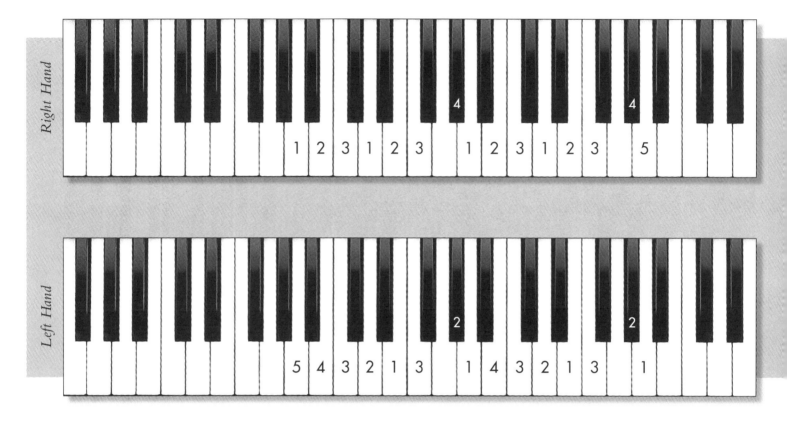

D MINOR HARMONIC SCALE

Hands separately: 2 Octaves. The left hand may start at the top or bottom of the scale at the candidate's choice.

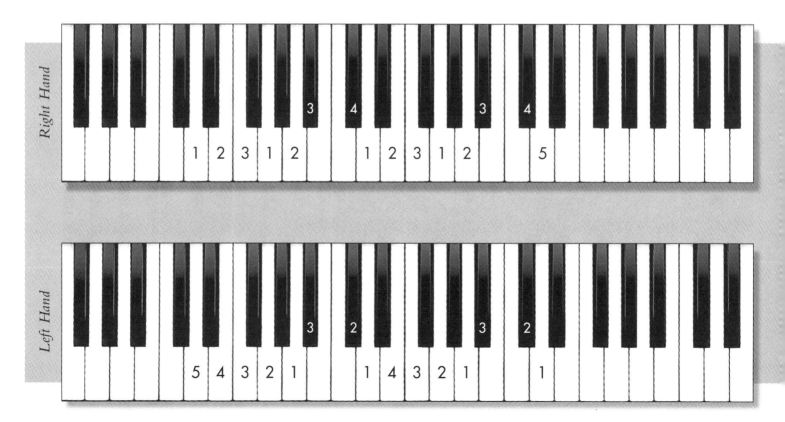

A MINOR MELODIC SCALE

Hands separately: 2 Octaves. The left hand may start at the top or bottom of the scale at the candidate's choice.
If starting at the top in the left hand melodic scales, follow the lower keyboard notation first.

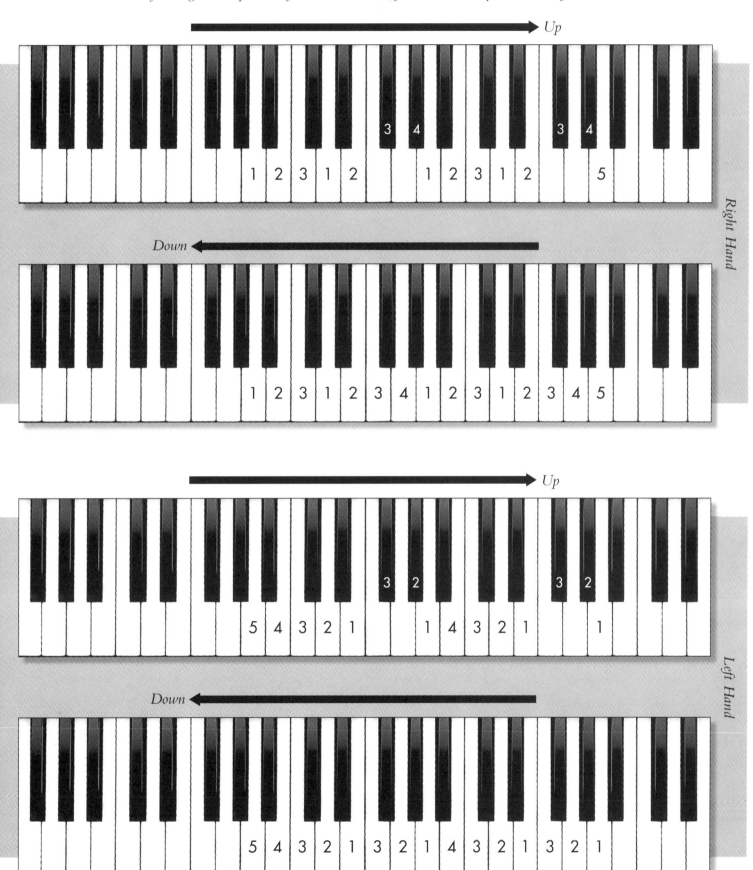

D MINOR MELODIC SCALE

Hands separately: 2 Octaves. The left hand may start at the top or bottom of the scale at the candidate's choice.
If starting at the top in the left hand melodic scales, follow the lower keyboard notation first.

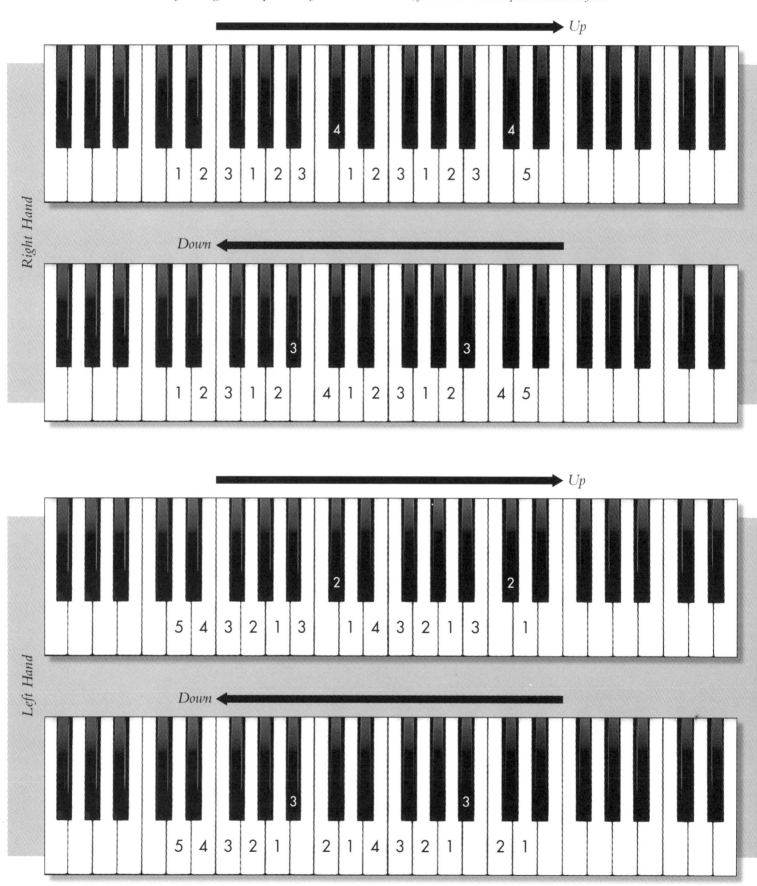

C MAJOR CONTRARY MOTION

Hands together beginning and ending on the key-note (unison): 1 Octave.
Notes played together with both hands are shown using the same geometric shape.

♩ = 60 *(minimum speed recommended by the ABRSM)*

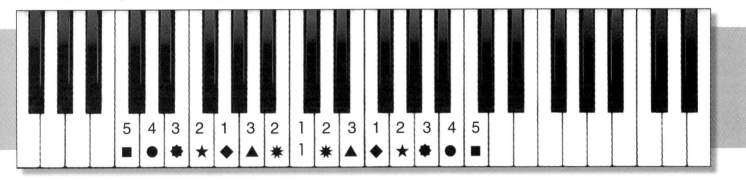

N.B. *The contrary motion scale is written without a time signature in groups of two quavers with the final note as a crotchet.*

C MAJOR ARPEGGIO

Hands separately: 1 Octave, up and down.
For the asterisked note in the left hand, 3 is an alternative.

♩. = 46 *(minimum speed recommended by the ABRSM)*

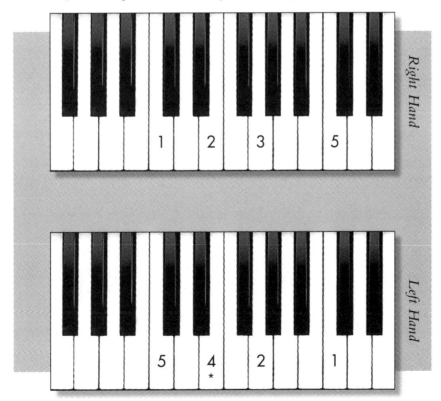

N.B. *The arpeggios are written using two bars of 6/8 time, in two groups of three quavers with the seventh note as a dotted crotchet followed by a dotted crotchet rest.*

G MAJOR ARPEGGIO

Hands separately: 1 Octave, up and down.
For the asterisked note in the left hand, 3 is an alternative.

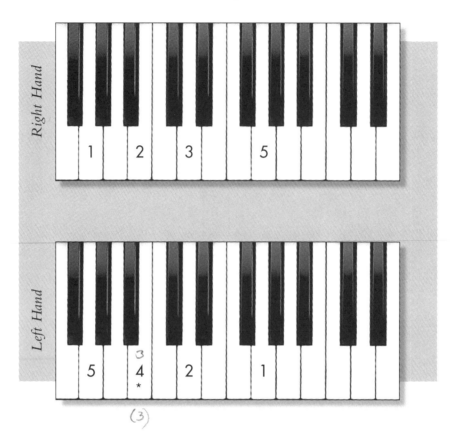

F MAJOR ARPEGGIO

Hands separately: 1 Octave, up and down.
For the asterisked note in the left hand, 3 is an alternative.

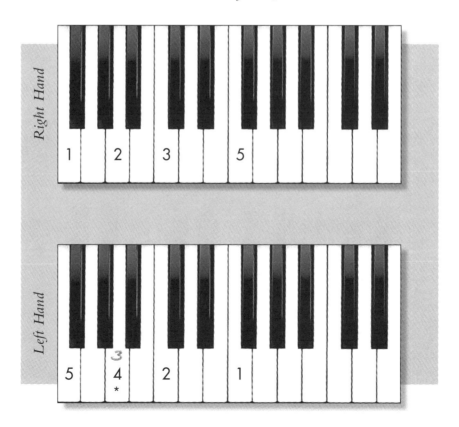

A MINOR ARPEGGIO

Hands separately: 1 Octave, up and down.
For the asterisked note in the left hand, 3 is an alternative.

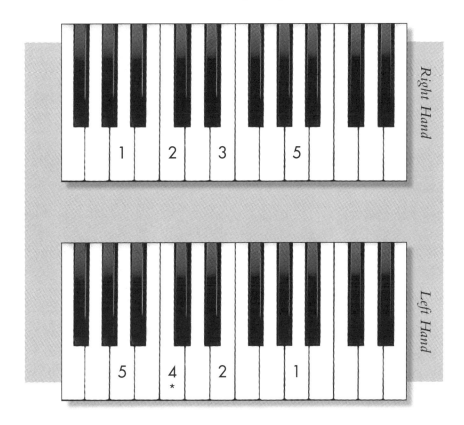

D MINOR ARPEGGIO

Hands separately: 1 Octave, up and down.
For the asterisked note in the left hand, 3 is an alternative.

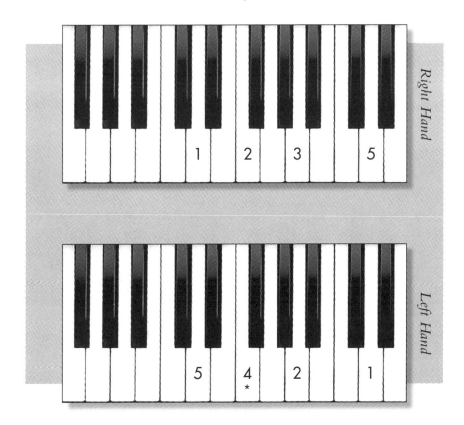

C MAJOR BROKEN CHORD

Hands separately. The pattern for broken chords is:

N.B. *The dotted crotchets should be given their full value.*

Left Hand

Right Hand

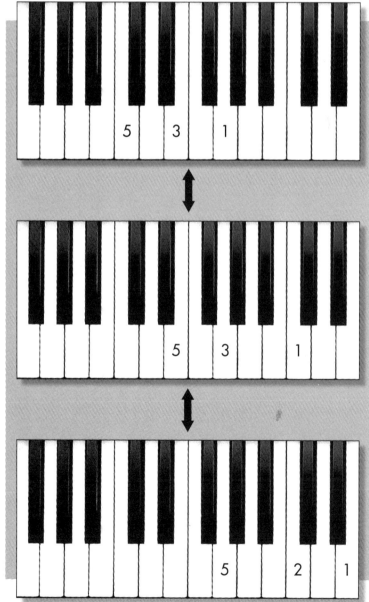

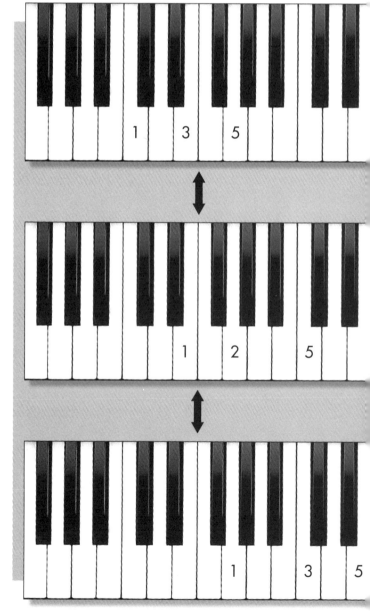

G MAJOR BROKEN CHORD

Hands separately. The pattern for broken chords is:

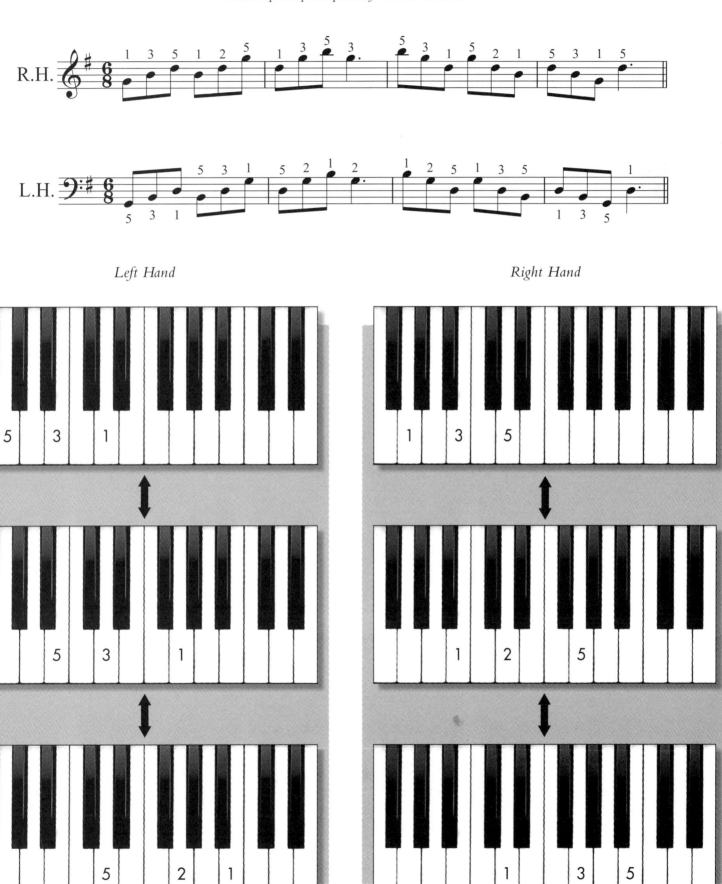

Left Hand

Right Hand

F MAJOR BROKEN CHORD

Hands separately. The pattern for broken chords is:

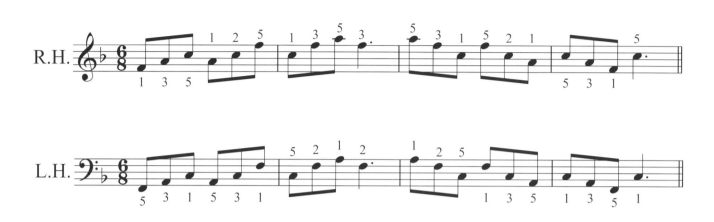

Left Hand   Right Hand

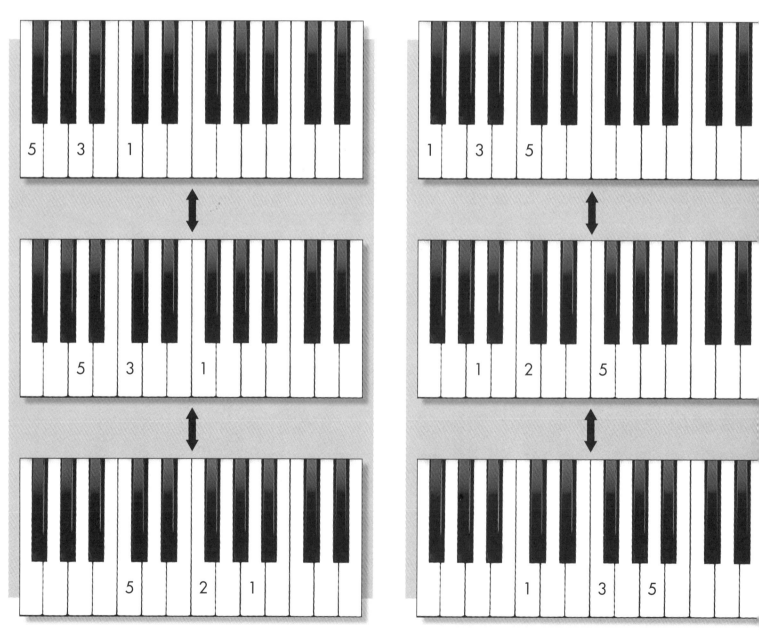

A MINOR BROKEN CHORD

Hands separately. The pattern for broken chords is:

Left Hand

Right Hand

D MINOR BROKEN CHORD

Hands separately. The pattern for broken chords is:

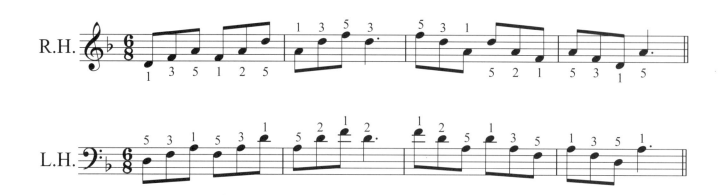

Left Hand   Right Hand

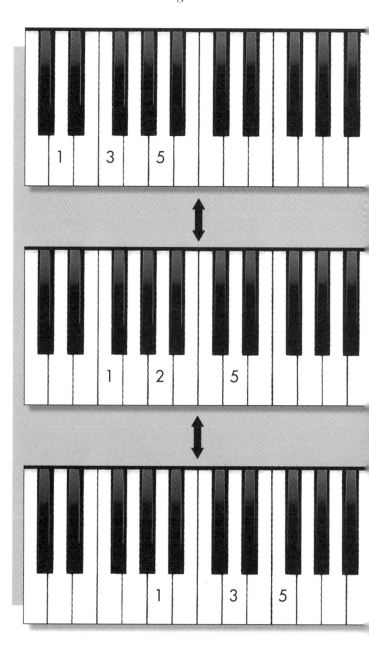